BAM!

The INCREDIBLE COMIC BOOK STUDIO

This action-packed book includes everything you need to create comic book superheroes and thrill-packed adventures.

•

At the back you will find stencils, awesome transfers, and plenty of pages to make your own comic book!

SPLAT

Hayley Down * Stuart Lynch

make believe ideas

WHAT'S INSIDE

CHAPTER 3
PLAN YOUR STORY

- PLOT YOUR STORY
- STORY PLANNER

CHAPTER 4
CREATE YOUR COMIC

- CREATING YOUR OWN COMIC GRID
- SOUND EFFECTS
- SPEECH, THOUGHTS, AND CAPTIONS
- CHOOSE YOUR WORDS WISELY!
- MAKE YOUR OWN COMIC BOOK

CHAPTER 1

CREATE YOUR SUPERHERO

Lab accidents are the number-one cause of superpowers!
Find a way through the maze to choose your character's power,
and then look up its incredible properties on the next page!

TIP!
You can travel under bridges.

START HERE

BEAKERS of **BULK**

GOGGLE BOGGLE

AMPHIBIOUS ANOMALY

BUNSEN BURNS

MENTAL MISHAP

TEST-TUBE TRANSFORMATION

So what amazing feats can (and can't) your superhero now perform?

BOP!

BIFF!

BEAKERS OF BULK

Your character is super strong and eats only veggies for extra power! Sadly, this character isn't too smart, so a clever assistant needs to be nearby.

KRRRASH!

MENTAL MISHAP

Your character can read minds and is an ultra-genius but can't throw a punch!

TEST-TUBE TRANSFORMATION

Your character can shoot a sticky gunge out of his hands – YUCK! Beware of water: It washes this superpower clean away.

GOGGLE BOGGLE

Your character has X-ray vision but needs strong glasses to read a newspaper!

AMPHIBIOUS ANOMALY

Your character can harness the power of water and ice! And breathing underwater is a breeze. Remember though, this superpower is useless away from water.

BUNSEN BURNS

Your character can harness the power of the sun. But saving the world once the sun goes down becomes very hard work.

The backstory RANDOM-ATOR

Your superhero's backstory tells us where he came from and explains his **motivation,** or the reason he is the way he is. Follow the arrows for a totally random route to your character's past.

START

Choose a number.
— 1 →
2
3

Red or blue?
red
blue

Choose a shape.

Art or sports?
art
sports

Cake or cookie?
cake
cookie

Day or night?
day
night

Choose a direction.
east
west
south
north

Monocle or pocket watch?
monocle
pocket watch

Salty or sweet?
salty
sweet

Choose a time.
4 p.m.
3 a.m.

Left or right?
left
right

'Beach or city?
beach
city

Brown or purple?
brown
purple

Summer or winter?
summer
winter

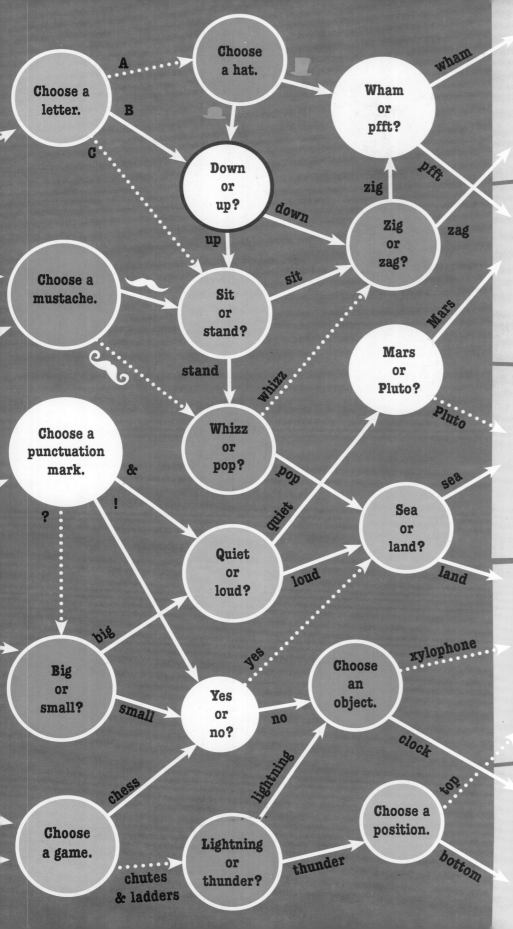

Choose a letter.
A ··· ▸ **Choose a hat.**
B
C ···

Choose a hat. ▸ **Down or up?**

Down or up?
up ▸ **Sit or stand?**
down ▸ **Zig or zag?**

Wham or pfft?
wham ▸ **Crime and punishment**
pfft ▸

Zig or zag?
zig ▸ **Wham or pfft?**
zag ▸

Choose a mustache. ▸ **Sit or stand?**

Sit or stand?
sit ▸ **Zig or zag?**
stand ▸ **Whizz or pop?**

Mars or Pluto?
Mars ▸
Pluto ··· ▸

Whizz or pop?
whizz ··· ▸ **Mars or Pluto?**
pop ▸ **Sea or land?**

Choose a punctuation mark.
& ▸ **Quiet or loud?**
! ▸
? ···

Quiet or loud?
quiet ▸ **Sea or land?**
loud ▸

Sea or land?
sea ▸ **Money and misery**
land ▸

Big or small?
big ▸
small ▸ **Yes or no?**

Yes or no?
yes ··· ▸ **Choose an object.**
no ▸

Choose an object.
xylophone ··· ▸
clock ▸

Choose a position.
top ···
bottom ▸

Choose a game.
chess ▸ **Yes or no?**
chutes & ladders ··· ▸ **Lightning or thunder?**

Lightning or thunder?
lightning ▸ **Choose an object.**
thunder ▸ **Choose a position.**

Crime and punishment
Your hero was once part of a criminal gang, crawling through cat doors to burgle the neighbors by day. Your hero escaped to build a new life with only one goal: to save the world!

Money and misery
Your hero grew up in a mansion with rich parents. Her parents disappeared on a cruise around Antarctica. Now your character lives in the mansion, fighting / masterminding crimes and hoping to find a clue to her parents' fate.

Clowning around town
Your hero grew up in a traveling circus. The tent was destroyed in a fire, and the acts parted ways. Your hero used his clown skills to get rich and famous. Now he brings the laughs by day and saves / destroys the world by night!

Out of this world!
Your hero lives a normal life, except for one thing: her family comes from outer space! They fled the doomed planet Tuck 100 years ago. Now enemy aliens are hunting them down – putting Earth in danger in the process!

Wild child
Your hero was raised by a pack of wild wolves. He spent ten years in the wild before being adopted by a passing explorer. Now your hero has amazing animal instincts that he can use for the good of mankind.

GOOD OR EVIL?

Superheroes dedicate their lives to saving the planet, but maybe your main character has evil plans in mind . . . or maybe he's just an ordinary Joe who finds himself in an extraordinary situation. Can't decide? Then answer the questions, adding the scores as you go. Read the result that matches your total.

START

Have you ever had an accident during a science experiment?
No, I'm good at science! (3)
Yes. (2)
No, I don't have accidents! (1)

You're at the cinema and the movie is boring. What do you do?
Throw popcorn at people's heads. (3)
Take a nap. (2)
Keep on watching – it might get better! (1)

You have homework due tomorrow. Do you . . .
do your homework? (3)
hang out with friends? (2)
OR
help your parents with chores? (1)

Who's your best friend?
Your mom (1)
Your teacher (3)
A school pal (2)

A lady falls over. Do you . . .
run away? (2)
LOL? (3)
OR
help her up? (1)

A sign says "Do not enter." Do you enter?
Only if somebody needs help inside. (1)
Yes, for the thrill of it! (3)
No, it says "Do NOT enter!" (2)

Do you eat your veggies?
Yes, they keep me strong! (1)
No, my minions eat them for me! (3)
Some of them. (2)

Which robot sounds coolest?
Protektor (1)
Ray-blast (2)
X-plodor (3)

Are you a millionaire?
Yes (3)
No (2)

Which place do you like best?
The park (2)
The beach (1)
The city (3)

What makes you happiest?
Kittens (3)
Puppies (1)
Money (2)

How do you laugh?
Ho-ho-ho! (1)
Ha-ha-ha! (2)
Mwah-ha-ha! (3)

What's your favorite food?
Pizza (2)
Chocolate cake (3)
Salad (1)

A sign says "Keep off the grass." Do you keep off the grass?
No, I don't listen to stupid signs! (3)
Yes, I don't want to squash a worm! (1)
Yes – and I yell at people who don't! (2)

How do you feel about littering?
NOO! I must protect our planet! (1)
I don't care – I'll destroy Earth anyway. (3)
Meh. (2)

Where do you sit when you get on a bus?
At the front, alone (1)
At the back with my pals (2)
I never catch the bus! (3)

How do you feel about ruling the world?
Finally! Bow down to me! (3)
With great power comes great responsibility. (1)
Meh. (2)

Your pet fish looks hungry. Do you . . .
feed it? (1)
ignore it? (2)
OR
eat it? (3)

Do you wash your hands after using the bathroom?
Yes (1)
No (3)
Maybe (2)

What kind of hat do you prefer?
Top hat (1)
Ski mask (3)
Baseball cap (2)

Describe your eyebrows.
Dark, skinny arches (3)
Bushy (1)
Normal! (2)

20–34
STRONG SUPERHERO

Your hero is physically perfect with a heart of gold. He has trouble making friends because he has to keep his identity secret, but he loves his mom more than anything. His hobbies include eating veggies (it's muscle food), exercising, and secret stake-outs!

35–49
AVERAGE JOE

The Average Joe is a reluctant hero. He'd prefer to chill with friends, but the world needs saving, and his do-gooder sidekick is really in charge! His hobbies include sleeping, chilling with friends, and hiding from his sidekick. Saving the world is a CHORE!

50–60
MASTER OF EVIL!

Your character is a rule-breaker, a loner, and – worst of all – PURE EVIL! He spends his days plotting and vanquishing enemies. His hobbies include stroking cats (a villain's best friend), bullying minions, and conducting crazy experiments.

What's their WEAKNESS?

Every superhero has a weakness that can threaten or destroy his powers. Choose one here!

Close your eyes, then swirl your finger around in the air and drop it on this page. The closest word will be your hero's weakness – just hope his nemesis doesn't find out!

BRIGHT LIGHTS

HEIGHTS

TOMATOES

RAINBOWS

THE COLOR GREEN

THE COLOR RED

MUD

LAVA

BUNNY RABBITS

PUPPIES

METEORIC ROCK

SNAKES

BAD BREATH

CEMENT!

COOKIES

MONSTERS

SPINACH

LATIN WORDS

THE DARK

NUTS

MOON ROCKS

The NAME GAME

Titles

Captain
Doctor
Professor
King   Lady
Man   Lord   Mr.
Boy   Major   Girl

Give your hero a "normal" name, and then give him a pseudonym – a fake name used to hide your hero's true identity.

The pseudonym should hint at your character's past and powers. Combine words from the arms of the stars to create your name.

Nature

Wave
Midnight
Earthquake
Starlight Magma
Shadow Beam Force
Forest Galaxy Boulder

Animals

Cheetah
Anaconda
Tarantula
Stallion Jackal
Dragon Viper Wolf
Kitten Shark Hawk

Weather

Thunder
Lightning
Blizzard
Hail Heat wave
Ice Breeze Mist
Storm Avalanche Flood

Colors

Red
Blue
Magenta
Green Violet
Amber Black Gray
White Gold Silver

NAME THE SUPERHEROES!

....

CHARACTER LOG

You're nearly ready to draw your hero. Before you start, record his details here.

HERO

REAL NAME	Austin
SUPER-NAME	king fire
SUPER-POWER	fire Powes
BACK-STORY	was Born in the fire nation
WEAKNESS	woter
ALL GOOD?	yes!

But wait, there's more! Does your superhero need a sidekick?

A sidekick is the hero's helper, or second in command. He may have superpowers, too. Profile him here.

SIDEKICK

REAL NAME	BoB
SUPER-NAME	cool DuDe
SUPER-POWER	air Bender
BACK-STORY	Parents Died
WEAKNESS	Rocks
ALL GOOD?	yes

You hero's **nemesis** is your story's baddie – as dedicated to evil deeds as your hero is to good ones. Maybe there is more than one.

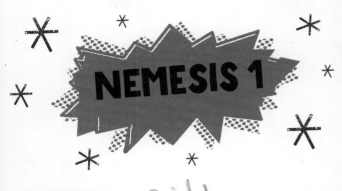

NEMESIS 1

REAL NAME Bill

NEMESIS NAME Dr. Bill

SUPER-POWER Smart

BACK-STORY Bill and Bob are Brothers

WEAKNESS Bad grades

ALL BAD? yes

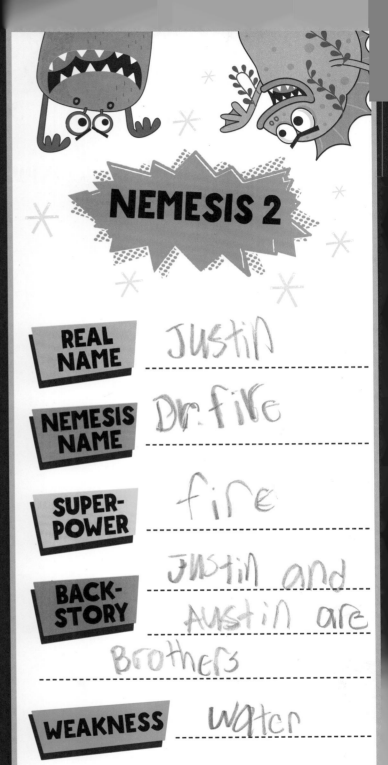

NEMESIS 2

REAL NAME Justin

NEMESIS NAME Dr. fire

SUPER-POWER fire

BACK-STORY Justin and Austin are Brothers

WEAKNESS water

ALL BAD? yes

CHAPTER

DRAW YOUR SUPERHERO

Here are some tips on getting the most from your stencils and transfers.

1 The stencils can be easily removed from the book and then pressed back in when you're finished.

2 Hold the stencil down firmly, and always use a pencil first so you can erase any mistakes!

3 You can see through your stencils. Look through them to join up body parts and position your drawings accurately.

4 Practice on scrap paper before filling in your comic panels.

These shapes can be combined to make awesome gadgets.

vehicles

arms and legs

These holes can help you create perfect comic strips.

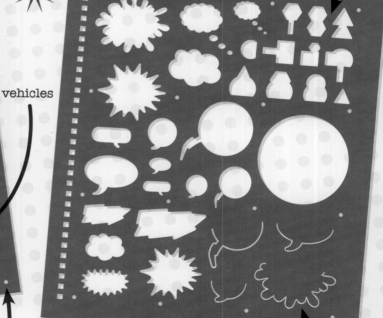

Use these shapes to create speech bubbles, sound effects, and more!

Your stencil has the parts you need to make the characters below.

You can try swapping heads, arms and legs between the characters to make even more combinations!

You'll continue to learn how to build cool characters over the next few pages.

TRANSFERS

1 Cut around the picture you want to transfer.

2 Pull off the plastic layer that holds the transfer, and then position it on your comic strip.

3 Rub the top of the transfer with a coin or something hard, making sure you rub over the entire image.

4 Lift the plastic from the paper to reveal the transferred image.

How to draw a
SUPERHERO BODY

Follow these simple steps to bring your characters to life!

1 Choose your body shape.

2 Using a pencil, lightly stencil the chosen body, making sure the edges of each shape meet.

3 Add the head.

4 Add the arms and legs. Flipping your stencil over helps make left or right limbs.

5 Draw a darker outline around your character.

6 Draw the hairline and face.

LOGO-A-GO-GO

You need to design your hero's super suit, but before you do that, you need a logo or symbol. A superhero's logo is an important part of his costume. It may also be projected into the sky, so it **HAS** to look good.

Letters are easy to draw and **clear** for the reader – try your hero's initials!

Contrasting colors help a symbol to stand out.

Symmetrical symbols can be easier to draw – try stars, triangles, or squares as your base shapes!

TRY DESIGNING SOME LOGOS HERE.

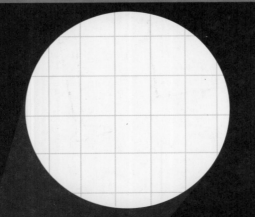

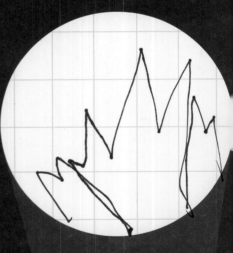

Choose a **shape** that links to your hero's pseudonym.

Now draw your character's logo in the sky sign.

SUIT UP!

Being a superhero takes more than just superpowers: you need a stylish super suit to really make an impact!

Follow the instructions below each character to finish these super-suit styles.

BUTT-KICKING
BODYSUIT

How do they get in and out of it? Nobody knows! But the bodysuit is easily worn under a hero's everyday clothes.

Create a dark outline for the outside of your drawing only.

•

Color the entire body in one shade

TIGHTY-WHITIES
OVER TIGHTS

A classic combo for super-strong heroes. Make sure you choose contrasting colors to make those underpants pop!

Fill the body, arms, and legs with the same color.

•

Color the underpants in a contrasting shade

LEOTARD AND TIGHTS

Is it a ballerina? Is it a gymnast? NO! It's a superhero! Stretchy tights are great for heroes with serious acrobatic skills.

Color the body in one shade.

•

Color the arms and legs with a different shade.

THE EVIL-NEMESIS COAT

A long coat can only mean one thing: your character is hiding something! These coats are easily lined with gadgets of all shapes and sizes.

Draw a border around the body of your character, this time drawing straight across the legs at the bottom.

•

Color your coat in any shade you want – darker looks scarier.

ACCESSORIZE!

Accessories can make or break a super suit!

CAPE

Draw freehand from your character's neck. Long capes are more dramatic. You can even do wavy hems.

GLOVES

Color your character's hands and forearms in a different shade. Choose any length you want.

BOOTS

Color your character's feet and shins in a different shade. Choose any length you want.

SKIRT

Draw freehand from your character's waist. Try different lengths and shapes.

MIGHTY MASKS

Study these cool **mask** designs, then create some of your own!

GET MOVING!

You can give your characters different body positions by changing the angle or direction of your stencils.

To change the position of your character's arms or legs, rotate your stencil, keeping it as close to the body you have drawn as possible.

Stencil the leg or arm, then look at your drawing. You might need to draw a small line freehand to connect the leg or arm to the body.

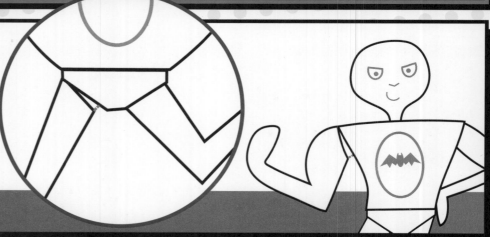

You can also change the size of your hero. Lightly stencil your character, and then draw inside or outside the line to make it bigger or smaller.

ACTION SHOT

Motion lines show a hero's movement. Look at the examples, and then try adding motion lines of your own!

CHARACTER BOOT CAMP

Use the next six pages to practice drawing superheroes, nemeses, and sidekicks!

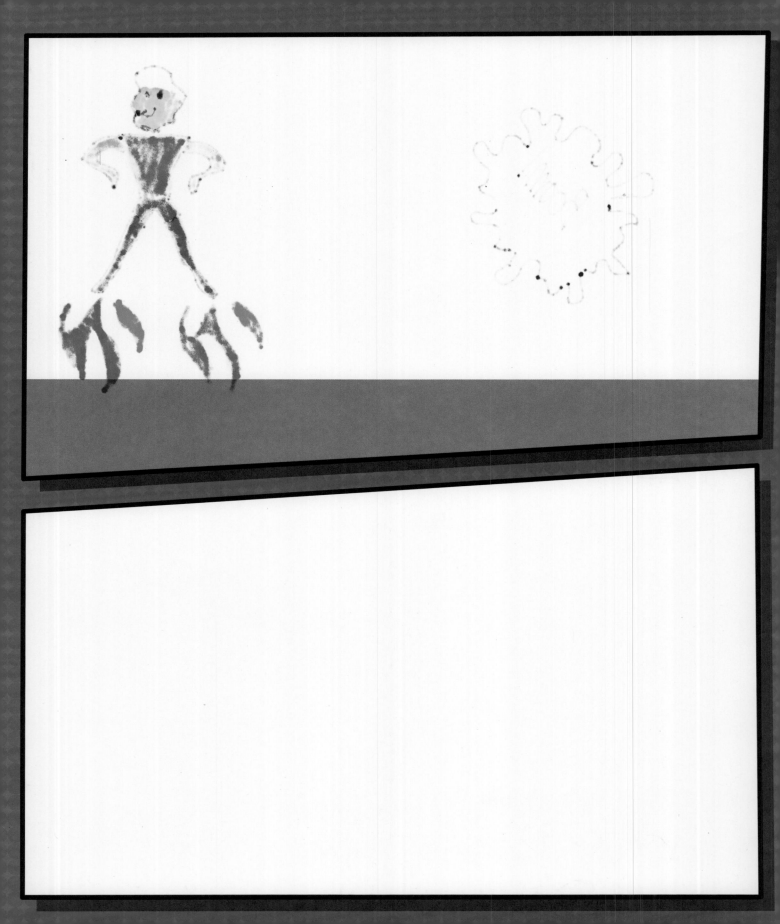

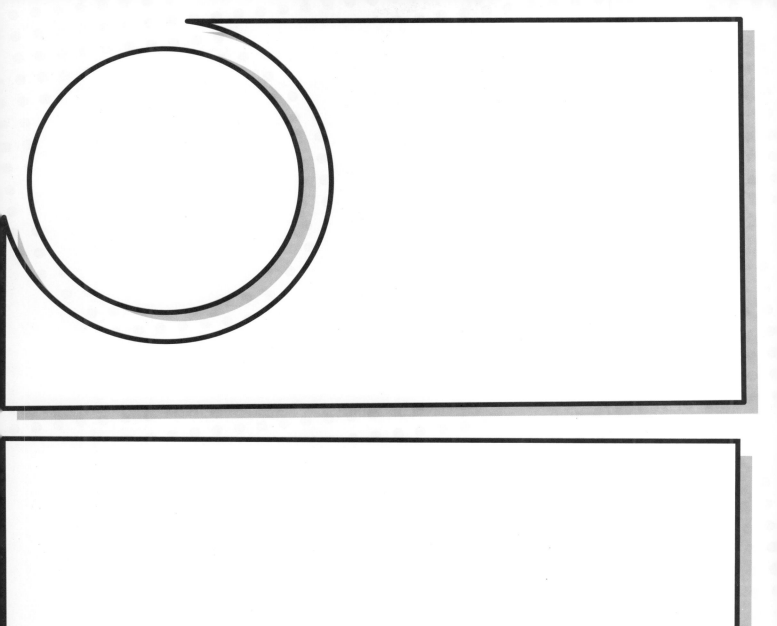

GADGET LAB!

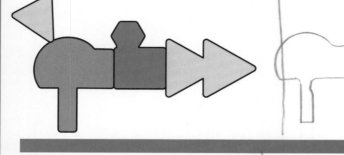

Name: Banana Blaster

Use: Shoots bananas to slip up enemies

Name: Gega Blasta

Use: Makes Big Boom's

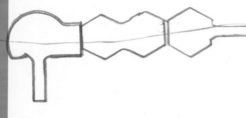

Name: Laser nater

Use: Shoots Lasers

Name: candy Blasta

Use: Shoots sticky gum

Name: ....   Name: ....

Use: ....   Use: ....

Name: ....   Name: ....

Use: ....   Use: ....

CUSTOM VEHICLES

You can use the stencil to draw the basic shapes for a helicopter, blimp, or rocket. Use the stencil shapes to customize the vehicles or turn them into land transportation.

Blimp

Rocket

Helicopter

STENCILS

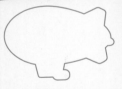

Blimp

Helicopter

Rocket

You could use the blimp stencil and add another stencil to the top to create a covert camera blimp!

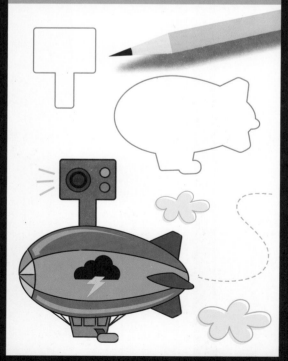

You could draw half of the rocket stencil and then add a circular stencil to create a superhero car!

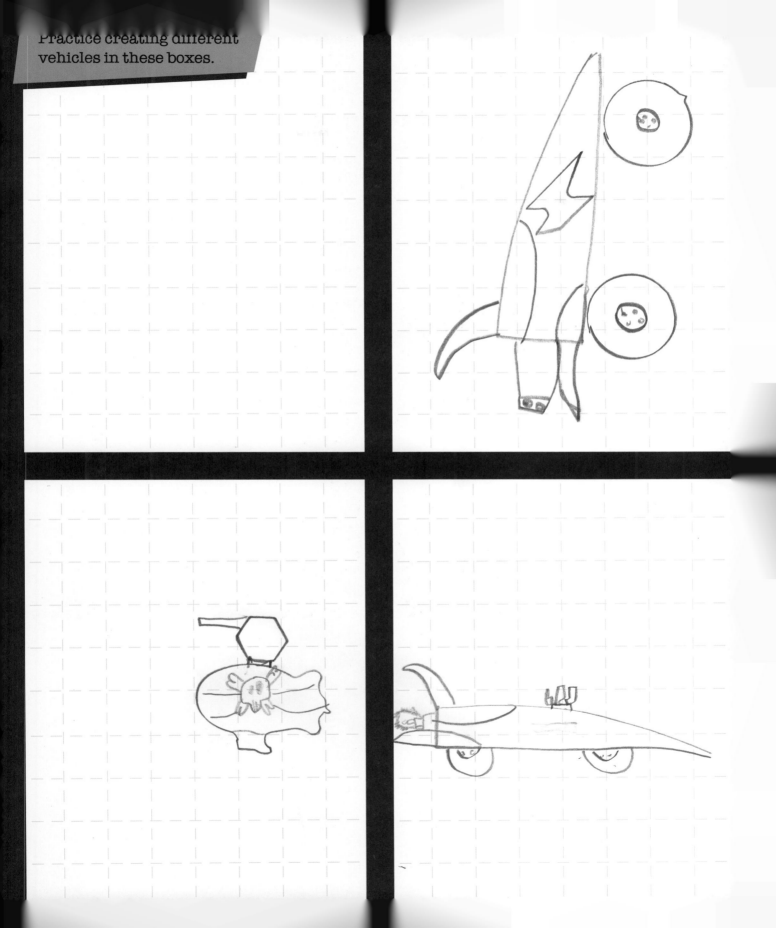

HQ, SWEET HQ!

Every superhero needs a secret headquarters for storing his tights!

Check the boxes to decide what kind of **HQ** your character will have, and then design the floor plan on the blueprints on the next page.

TYPE:

hollow volcano ☐

alleyway ☐

underground sewers ☐

basement of your mansion ☐

cottage ☐

underwater office ☐

a blimp ☐

Add your own!

------------------------ ------------------------

------------------------ ------------------------

LOCATION:

city ☐   jungle ☐

countryside ☐   forest ☐

North Pole ☐   sky ☐

tropical island ☑   the moon ☐

CHOOSE THE PASSWORD FOR ENTRY:

Fire 9999

WHAT'S INSIDE?

uniform lockers ☑   gadget storeroom ☑

dungeon ☐   CCTV monitors ☐

helipad ☐   gym ☑

pontoon / dock ☐   swimming pool ☑

garage for vehicles ☑   kitchen ☑

Add your own!

------------------------ ------------------------

------------------------ ------------------------

HERE'S AN EXAMPLE HQ!

bedroom

satellite communication room

indoor swimming pool

kitchen

training room

gym

living area

secret escape | costumes and masks | main entrance

PLOT YOUR STORY

Now you're ready to create your story!

Before you start, think about the whole story. If you're stuck for ideas, choose a mystery object from this grab bag. Then read the panel with the matching number on the next page.

① tools

② handcuffs

③ kitten

④ Statue of Liberty

⑤ clock

⑥ trash can

⑦ kaleidoscope

1

A local inventor has just announced his newest creation: the Superbot! Your hero's nemesis steals the Superbot and reprograms it to carry out his evil plans. Can you stop the Superbot in time and turn it back into a force for good?

5

The world goes into meltdown when the clocks start moving backward! Daily routines are turned on their head as breakfast becomes dinner and Thursday becomes Wednesday. Is the world really moving back in time? Who caused the chaos? Can your hero get time moving in the right direction again?

2

Your hero's nemesis has hatched a plan to steal your sidekick's powers! When your sidekick is busy helping an old lady across the road, he is handcuffed by a baddie posing as a police officer and taken to the nemesis's lair. How will your hero rescue him, and will he be in time to save his sidekick's superpowers?

6

Everyone is confused when their cans start moving, then terrified when they realize there is something inside the cans watching their every move! Only your hero is brave enough to open the lid – but what will he find inside?

3

Your hero's nemesis has transformed himself into a harmless looking kitten and has been adopted by the president as the White House pet! Will your hero discover the truth about the clandestine kitty before America's secrets are stolen?

7

Your hero gets a strange package in the post: a kaleidoscope! When he looks though the eye hole, a message appears in the shapes. Somebody needs your hero's help – but who? And how will he help them?

4

Famous landmarks from around the world have gone missing. Your hero discovers that her nemesis is stealing tourist attractions to create a replica world. This evil plan must be stopped before there are no attractions left and everyone's vacations are ruined!

STORY PLANNER

TITLE _____

CHARACTERS _____

_____

_____

PANEL NUMBER	WHAT HAPPENS

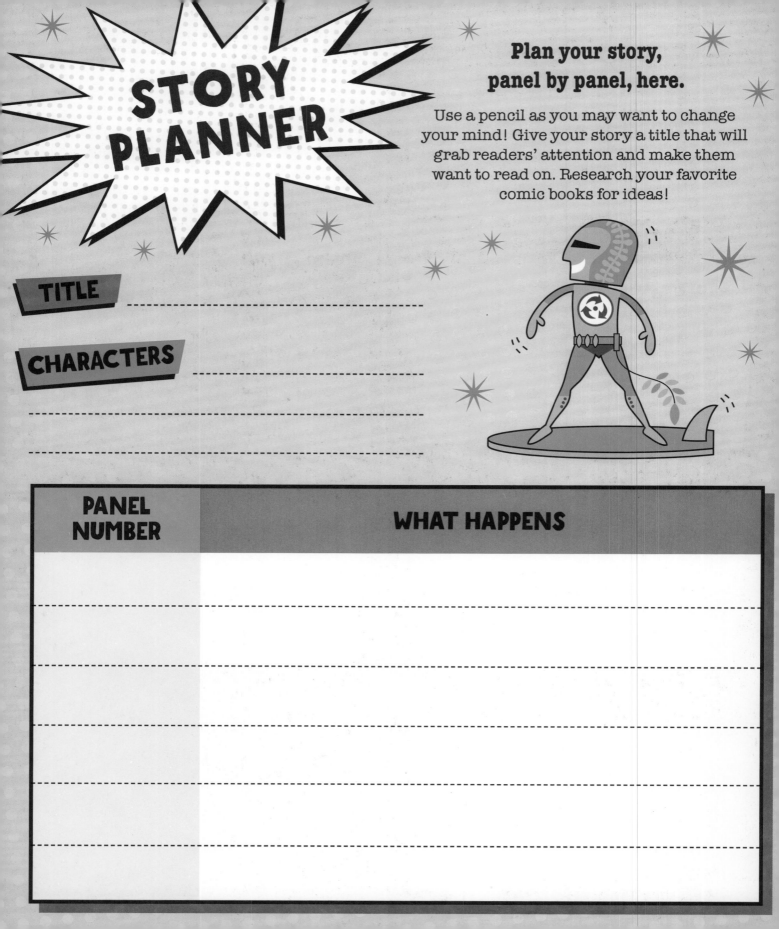

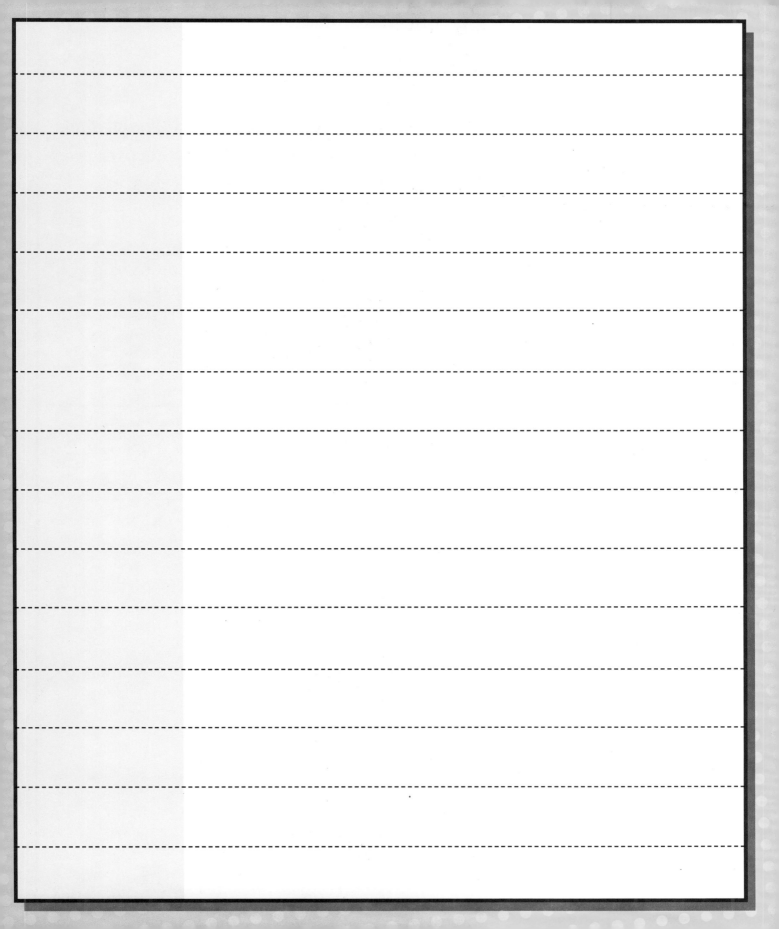

Creating your own
COMIC GRID

Follow these instructions to create your own comic grids.

BASIC GRID

1 Stencil dots through the holes.

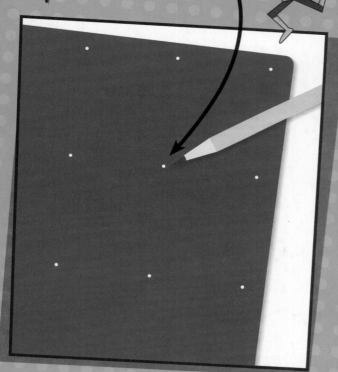

2 Lift the stencil, and use the straight edge to draw lines that join the dots to create the perfect panel.

TO CREATE LARGER BOXES

1 Stencil dots through the holes as before.

2 Lift the stencil, and use the straight edge to join up the dots, drawing a downward border only every two dots to make a double-sized box.

SPEECH, THOUGHTS, AND CAPTIONS

Each part of a comic strip has a name and a special function.

The boxes that make up a comic strip are called panels.

Thought bubbles (or balloons) hold a character's thoughts and look like clouds.

A **caption** fits in the corner of a panel. It sets the scene for what is happening.

Speech bubbles (or balloons) are spoken words and can be different shapes.

That's a big monster! Quick! Let's get out of here!

Have you seen my tights?

Pass me the gunge blaster!

Use your stencils to create speech and thought bubbles of your own.

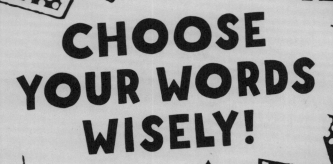

CHOOSE YOUR WORDS WISELY!

Choose your words carefully when you fill your speech and thought bubbles. You don't have much room, so every word counts! Keep dialogue simple but interesting enough to make the reader want to see what happens next!

Example 1 is filled in for you. Read the descriptions, and then fill in the bubbles in stages 2, 3, and 4.

STAGE 1

This stage introduces the hero's backstory. He worked for a circus until a mysterious fire meant the performers went their separate ways.

The nemesis is introduced. Here, the hero is busy at his job in a pet shop when it is raided. The hero saves the day, but will his nemesis return?

STAGE 4

This is a dramatic scene. The heroes encounter their nemesis, and a battle ensues. The gadgets come out, but to the heroes' surprise, their nemesis disappears.

MAKE YOUR OWN COMIC BOOK

Use these pages to create your book. Draw your own grid shapes, or use the dots on your stencils as a guide. You can write your title in the first panel, across the top of the page, or across the entire front cover.

1 Pull out two or more pages and cut along the dotted lines.

2 Stack the pages together, and turn the book over.

3 Fold the jutting-out rectangle over, and tape it down to hold your pages together.